Look What God Made!

L.J. Sattgast

Illustrations by Janet McDonnell

To the Parent

Sometimes we need a reminder to look around
at the beautiful world God made. When we take
the time to enjoy it, we're likely to have the
same reaction He had:

God saw all that he had made, and it was very good.

—*Gen. 1:31*

Chariot Books™
A Division of Cook Communications

Five sleepy children would rather stay
In their nice warm covers at the break of day.
All but the little one, who jumped out of bed
Ran to the window, and clapped as he said—

"Look what *God* made!"

Five happy children went out to play
With the barnyard cats in the
    sweet-smelling hay.
They climbed up a rope that was
    big and stout
And that's when the little one began
    to shout—

"Look what *God* made!"

Five curious children followed some tracks,
Heard a soft rustle, and a loud Quack! Quack!
They crept through the rushes and what did
they find?
"WOW!" yelled Mo
Who was last in line—

"Look what *God* made!"

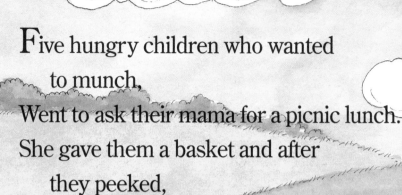

Five hungry children who wanted
    to munch,
Went to ask their mama for a picnic lunch.
She gave them a basket and after
    they peeked,
They all gave a cheer
But the little one squeaked—

Five brave children, as strong as can be
Decided to climb up the apple tree.
The little one hollered, "Wait for me!"
Then he stopped and whispered,
"Do you see what *I* see?"

"Something *God* made!"

Five noisy children romp and play
But only 'til they hear their mama say,
"Put on your pajamas. It's time for bed!"
Then they ran to get ready
And guess who said—

"Look what *God* made!"

Five tired children crawled into bed
As soon as all their prayers were said.
Up went the covers and down went the sun
And no one saw
What God had done . . .

But the little one!